# Mermaid Fun

Written by Lisa Thompson
Pictures by Craig Smith

"I can dive,"
said the mermaid.

"I can swim,"
said the mermaid.

4

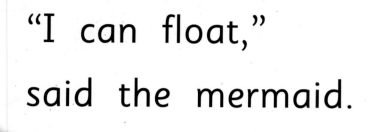

"I can float,"
said the mermaid.

"I can dance,"
said the mermaid.

8

"I can jump,"
said the mermaid.

10

"I can hide,"
said the mermaid.

12

"I can play hide and seek," said the mermaid.